PES
CONTROL

Alison Hawes

Illustrated by Paul Savage

Titles in First Flight

Badger Publishing Limited
15 Wedgwood Gate, Pin Green Industrial Estate,
Stevenage, Hertfordshire SG1 4SU
Telephone: 01438 356907. Fax: 01438 747015
www.badger-publishing.co.uk
enquiries@badger-publishing.co.uk

Pest Control ISBN 1 84424 818 6

Text © Alison Hawes 2006
Complete work © Badger Publishing Limited 2006

Series Editor: Jonny Zucker
Publisher: David Jamieson
Commissioning Editor: Carrie Lewis
Editor: Paul Martin
Design: Fiona Grant
Illustration: Paul Savage

PEST CONTROL

Alison Hawes

Contents

New Boys

Lee was new to Upton.
Lee and his kid brother, Mark,
had just moved house.

Their mum and dad had new jobs
in Upton. And Lee and Mark had
started at a new school.

Lee and Mark's new school was
Greenway School.

Lee was in Mr Jack's class. He made
lots of friends in his very first week.

In fact, Lee was happy with his new home, his new school and his new friends.

He liked it all – all except Nick and Josh, that is.

But then, no-one liked Nick and Josh much!

Nick and Josh were the class pests.
They liked to play tricks on people.

They thought they were so funny!
But they were not.

Sometimes they took people's things.

Sometimes they tripped people up.

Sometimes they messed up people's work.

And sometimes they told fibs just to get people into trouble!

Lee and his friends did their best
to keep out of Nick and Josh's way.
And for weeks, Nick and Josh left
them alone.

But then, Lee saw Nick and Josh
picking on his kid brother.

Lee was so angry, he ran up to Nick and Josh.

"Stop it! Leave him alone!" he said. "He's just a kid!"

But Nick and Josh wouldn't leave Mark alone.

Lee didn't know what to do.

In the end, Lee told Mr Jack.

But Nick and Josh just stopped picking on Mark and started picking on Lee instead!

Out of Order!

Day after day, Nick and Josh
did lots of little things to upset Lee.

Sometimes, they hid his kit bag,
so he couldn't play football.

Or they knocked his arm, so he
messed up his work.

Day after day, they did lots of little things that made Lee angry.

Sometimes, they grabbed his lunch box and played catch with it. When they gave it back, his lunch was a mess.

Lee just wanted Nick and Josh to stop. But he didn't know what to do.

In the end, he smiled and said, "Well, if they play tricks on me, then I will play tricks on them!"

One day, Nick and Josh were
standing outside the toilets.
They stopped Lee going in.

"You can't go in there!" said Nick.

"No," grinned Josh. "The toilets are
out of order!"

Lee was cross.

He knew it was just a trick.
But he needed to go to the toilet!

His friends wanted him to tell
Mr Jack. But Lee smiled and
said, "No, I have got an idea!"

Lee looked at Nick and Josh and he smiled.

"I'll just use the girls' toilets then," he said, "until the boys' toilets are fixed!"

Lee's friends thought this was funny. They laughed and laughed at Nick.

But Nick was very, very angry!
He did not like people laughing
at him.

"I'll get that new boy!" he said to
Josh. "I'm going to get him big
time. Just you see, if I don't!"

Pay up!

A week later it was Nick's birthday. He got a new digital camera for his birthday.

He brought it into school and took photos of all the kids in the playground.

Then Nick let Lee
have a go with
his camera.

Lee took the camera.

He took a photo but the camera
didn't work! He could not
understand it!

Then Lee saw Josh wink at Nick.
He saw Josh put something
in his pocket.

So he knew that Nick and Josh
were playing a trick on him.

"Just look at my new camera!" said Nick. "It won't work! You will have to pay for it to be fixed!"

"Yes!" said Josh. "You will have to pay!"

Lee didn't know what to do.
That night, at home,
he could not sleep.

He could not sleep until he thought
of a trick to play on Nick and Josh!

The next day, Lee brought some money into school. Nick grabbed the money and put it in his pocket.

"This is the best trick ever!" Nick said to Josh.

And they laughed and laughed.

At the end of school, Nick and Josh ran to the shop to spend the money.

But when they went to pay, they got a shock.

"I cannot take this money!" said the shopkeeper. "These are not £1 coins!"

Nick and Josh looked at the money.

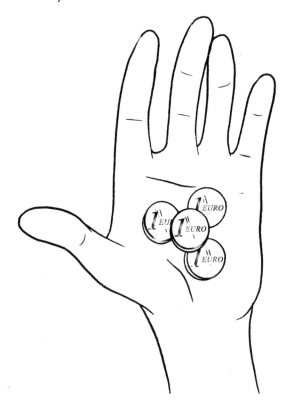

Lee had tricked them again! Nick and Josh were very angry with Lee. They did not like it when people played tricks on them!

The next day, Nick and Josh were still very angry with Lee.

So they made a sign to put on Lee's back.

Lee's friends saw the sign.
They took it off and showed it
to Lee.

At first, Lee was angry. But then
he smiled. He had a plan.

Lee took a pen from his bag.
He crossed out the letters C and
K on the sign. Then he put two
new letters on the sign.

He showed it to his friends.
They laughed and laughed.

In the playground, all the girls
ran after Nick. He could not
understand it!

Then Josh saw the sign on Nick's
back. He thought it was very
funny! He laughed and laughed.

At last, Josh took the sign down
from Nick's back. And at last, Nick
saw what the sign said.

Nick did not like being laughed at.
He was very, very angry with Lee.

"I don't know what to do!" said Nick. "When we play a trick on Lee, he just plays a trick on us!"

They thought and thought about what to do.

But in the end, they just gave up and left Lee alone at last!